# THE DINOSAUR SEARCH & FIND BOOK

By
Tony and Tony
Tallarico

kidsbooks
Incorporated

# FAST-FOODASAURUS

## FIND THESE ITEMS:

- ☐ Banana peel
- ☐ Bat
- ☐ Bell
- ☐ Beret
- ☐☐ Bones
- ☐ Book
- ☐ Bow tie
- ☐ Broken balloon
- ☐ Cactus
- ☐ Candle
- ☐ Chef
- ☐ Crayon
- ☐ Envelope
- ☐ Eyeglasses
- ☐☐ Fish
- ☐ Flower
- ☐ Football
- ☐ Heart
- ☐ Key
- ☐ Lost sock
- ☐ Mouse hole
- ☐ Mushroom
- ☐ Music note
- ☐ Net
- ☐ Rabbit
- ☐ Saw
- ☐ Scarf
- ☐ Star
- ☐ Sunglasses
- ☐ Tattoo
- ☐ Toothbrush
- ☐ Umbrella
- ☐ Whistle

# FAMILY REUNION PORTRAIT-ASAURUS

## FIND THESE ITEMS:

- ☐ Baseball
- ☐ Baseball bat
- ☐☐ Baseball caps
- ☐ Brush
- ☐ Cactus
- ☐ Candle
- ☐ Coffee cup
- ☐ Coffee pot
- ☐ Cookie
- ☐ Egg
- ☐ Eyeglasses
- ☐ Football
- ☐ Fish
- ☐ Flower
- ☐ Heart
- ☐ Horseshoe
- ☐ Mouse
- ☐ Moustache
- ☐ Pear
- ☐ Ring
- ☐ Rollerskate
- ☐ Sleeping dino
- ☐☐ Stars
- ☐ Straw
- ☐ Yo-yo
- ☐ Who is ordering pizza?

# SKI
## -A-
## SAURUS
## MOUNTAIN

**FIND ALL THE LETTERS OF THE ALPHABET:**

❑ A
❑ B
❑ C
❑ D
❑ E
❑ F
❑ G
❑ H
❑ I
❑ J
❑ K
❑ L
❑ M
❑ N
❑ O
❑ P
❑ Q
❑ R
❑ S
❑ T
❑ U
❑ V
❑ W
❑ X
❑ Y
❑ Z

-AND-

❑ Baseball hat
❑ Flower
❑ Heart
❑ Pizza delivery dino
❑ Star

# THE DUNCE-A-SAURUS CLUB

**FIND THESE ITEMS:**

- ❏ Apple
- ❏ Banana peel
- ❏ Barber pole
- ❏ Baseball bat
- ❏ Birdcage
- ❏ Cactus
- ❏ Capless dino
- ❏ Cupcake
- ❏ Fire Hydrant
- ❏ Fish
- ❏ Flower
- ❏ Ghost
- ❏ Golf club
- ❏ Ice cream cone
- ❏ Kite
- ❏ Mailbox
- ❏ Mouse hole
- ❏❏ Moustaches
- ❏ Paintbrush
- ❏ Pencil
- ❏ Quarter moon
- ❏ Rabbit
- ❏ Ring
- ❏ Scarf
- ❏ Seal
- ❏ Star
- ❏ Teepee
- ❏ Thermometer
- ❏ Watermelon slice
- ❏ Whale

# SHOP-A-HOLIC-SAURUS

## FIND THESE ITEMS:

- ☐☐☐☐☐ Arrows
- ☐☐ Books
- ☐ Bird
- ☐ Broken bulb
- ☐ Bubble gum bubble
- ☐ Cane
- ☐ Coffee cup
- ☐ Cap
- ☐ Ear muffs
- ☐ Fish
- ☐ Football
- ☐ Hat
- ☐ Lost Balloon
- ☐ Lost sock
- ☐ Mailbox
- ☐ Music note
- ☐ Newspaper reader
- ☐ Pencil
- ☐ Phonograph
- ☐ Rocking chair
- ☐☐ Scarves
- ☐ Shoulder bag
- ☐ Star
- ☐☐☐☐ Tires
- ☐☐ Trash cans
- ☐ Umbrella
- ☐ Vacant store
- ☐ Water fountain

# MT. VOLCANOSAURUS

### FIND THESE ITEMS:

- ☐ Automobile
- ☐ Banana
- ☐ Bat
- ☐ Bath brush
- ☐ Beachball
- ☐ Boot
- ☐ Carrot
- ☐ Clothespin
- ☐ Cow
- ☐ Crayon
- ☐ Daisy
- ☐ Dart
- ☐ Fish
- ☐ Football
- ☐ Ghost
- ☐ Hockey stick
- ☐ Humpty Dumpty
- ☐☐ Keys
- ☐ Kite
- ☐ Lightbulb
- ☐ Octopus
- ☐☐ Pumpkins
- ☐ Rabbit
- ☐ Rooster
- ☐ TV set
- ☐ Sand pail
- ☐ Sock
- ☐ Telescope
- ☐ Ten-gallon hat
- ☐ Toothpaste tube
- ☐ Umbrella

**FIND THESE ITEMS:**

- ☐☐ Arrows
- ☐ Baseball cap
- ☐ Beret
- ☐☐ Bones
- ☐ Bouquet of flowers
- ☐ Burned-out bulb
- ☐ Escaped balloon
- ☐ Feather
- ☐ Football
- ☐ Ice cream cone
- ☐ Hammer
- ☐ Heart
- ☐ Hotdog
- ☐ Lost shoe
- ☐ Microphone
- ☐ Moustache
- ☐ Pearls
- ☐ Pencil
- ☐ Pizza
- ☐ Scissors
- ☐ Screwdriver
- ☐☐ Stars
- ☐☐ Sunglasses
- ☐ Telescope
- ☐ Who ordered the pizza?
- ☐ Yo-yo

# AIRPORT -A- SAURUS

## FIND THESE ITEMS:

- ☐ Accordian
- ☐ Arrow
- ☐ Book
- ☐ Bow tie
- ☐ Candy cane
- ☐ Crown
- ☐ Eyeglasses
- ☐ Flying carpet
- ☐ Flying elephant
- ☐ Flying fish
- ☐ Flying saucer
- ☐ Football
- ☐ Hatbox
- ☐ Heart
- ☐ Hot air balloon
- ☐ Hot dog
- ☐ Ice cream pop
- ☐ Kite
- ☐ Paper airplane
- ☐ Periscope
- ☐ Pizza box
- ☐☐ Propellers
- ☐ Roller skates
- ☐ Sailor cap
- ☐ Star
- ☐ Straw
- ☐ Top hat
- ☐ Umbrella
- ☐ Watering can
- ☐☐ Yo-yo's

# SENIOR-CITIZEN-SAURUS

## FIND THESE ITEMS:

- ☐ Anchor
- ☐ Apple
- ☐☐ Balls
- ☐ Balloon
- ☐ Banana
- ☐ Bow tie
- ☐☐ Canes
- ☐ Coffee pot
- ☐ Coon skin cap
- ☐ Crown
- ☐ Cup
- ☐ Drum
- ☐☐☐☐ Eyeglasses
- ☐ Feather
- ☐ High-heeled shoes
- ☐ Kite
- ☐ Moustache
- ☐☐☐ Neckties
- ☐ Paddle
- ☐ Paintbrush
- ☐ Pencil
- ☐ Pocketbook
- ☐ Propeller
- ☐ Ring
- ☐ Sailboat
- ☐ Sailor cap
- ☐ Skateboard
- ☐ Sunglasses
- ☐ Top hat
- ☐ Turtle
- ☐ Yo-yo

## CYBER-SAURUS

**FIND THESE ITEMS:**

- ☐ Apple core
- ☐ Baseball
- ☐ Baseball bat
- ☐ Cactus
- ☐ Drum
- ☐ Elephant
- ☐ Eyeglasses
- ☐ Fish
- ☐ Flower
- ☐ Ghost
- ☐ Hamburger
- ☐☐☐ Hearts
- ☐ Horse
- ☐ Igloo
- ☐ Jester
- ☐ Knitting needle
- ☐ Laundry
- ☐ Lion
- ☐ Mouse
- ☐ Moustache
- ☐ Net
- ☐ Oil can
- ☐ Pencil
- ☐ Penguin
- ☐ Plunger
- ☐ Rabbit

MULTI-
CINEMA-
SAURUS

**FIND THESE ITEMS:**

- ☐ Backpack
- ☐ Balloon
- ☐ Bird
- ☐ Bowling bag
- ☐☐☐☐ Burned-out lightbulbs
- ☐ Cane
- ☐ Cell phone
- ☐ Dollar bill
- ☐☐ Flower pots
- ☐ Football helmet
- ☐ Gum
- ☐☐☐ Hearts
- ☐ Ice cream pop
- ☐ Lollipop
- ☐ Missing lightbulb
- ☐ Necktie
- ☐ Pillow
- ☐ Rollerskate
- ☐ Scooter
- ☐ Straw
- ☐ Suspenders
- ☐ "3"
- ☐ Toothbrush
- ☐ Top hat
- ☐ Turban
- ☐ Umbrella
- ☐ Volcano

# WELCOME TO THE TRIVIA-SAURUS CONVENTION

## FIND THESE ITEMS:

- ☐ Astronaut
- ☐ Automobile
- ☐ Banana peel
- ☐ Baseball cap
- ☐ Bat
- ☐ Book
- ☐ Candle
- ☐ Candy cane
- ☐ Cup
- ☐ Eyeglasses
- ☐ Feather
- ☐ Flower
- ☐ Ghost
- ☐☐☐☐ Hearts
- ☐ Ice cream pop
- ☐ Ice skates
- ☐ Jack-o-lantern
- ☐☐ Keys
- ☐ Necktie
- ☐ Pencil
- ☐ Pizza delivery dino
- ☐ Pointy beard
- ☐ Propeller
- ☐ Purse
- ☐ Rabbit
- ☐ Rollerskate
- ☐ Scarf
- ☐ Sunglasses
- ☐ Volcano
- ☐ Yo-yo

# LUNCH ROOM -A- SAURUS

## FIND THESE ITEMS:

- ☐ Alien
- ☐ Backpack
- ☐ Banana peel
- ☐☐ Bones
- ☐ Broken heart
- ☐ Broom
- ☐ Candle
- ☐ Cell phone
- ☐ Cook
- ☐ Dunce cap
- ☐ Fire hydrant
- ☐ Fish
- ☐ Football helmet
- ☐ Guitar
- ☐ Hammer
- ☐ Ice cream cone
- ☐ Music note
- ☐ Necktie
- ☐ Old tire
- ☐ Paper airplane
- ☐☐☐ Pencils
- ☐ Periscope
- ☐ Santa cap
- ☐ Skate
- ☐ Skateboard
- ☐ Sock
- ☐ Umbrella
- ☐ Worm
- ☐ Who is ordering pizza?

# FARM -A- SAURUS

## FIND THESE ITEMS:

- ☐ Axe
- ☐ Balloon
- ☐ Candy cane
- ☐ Coffee pot
- ☐ Cow
- ☐☐☐ Crayons
- ☐☐☐☐☐☐ Crows
- ☐ Dog
- ☐ Duck
- ☐ Empty flower pot
- ☐ Golf club
- ☐ Hoe
- ☐ Horseshoe
- ☐ Ice cream cone
- ☐ Key
- ☐ Kite
- ☐ Mouse
- ☐ Neckerchief
- ☐ Pencil
- ☐ Pear
- ☐ Pig
- ☐ Pitchfork
- ☐ Rooster
- ☐ Shovel
- ☐ Snake
- ☐ Star
- ☐ Tic-tac-toe
- ☐☐☐☐☐☐ Tires
- ☐ Toothbrush
- ☐ Top hat
- ☐ Turtle
- ☐ Watering can
- ☐ Wristwatch

# SKATE-BOARD -A- SAURUS

## FIND THESE ITEMS:

- ☐ Auto
- ☐ Band-aid
- ☐ Banana peel
- ☐ Baseball cap
- ☐ Broken heart
- ☐ Cactus
- ☐ Doghouse
- ☐☐ Fish
- ☐ Flashlight
- ☐ Ghost
- ☐ Hammer
- ☐ Helmet
- ☐ Lost shoe
- ☐ Motorized board
- ☐ Mushroom
- ☐ Pencil
- ☐ Periscope
- ☐ Pie
- ☐ Pizza
- ☐ Pogo stick
- ☐ Ring
- ☐ Scarf
- ☐ Shark fin
- ☐ Sled
- ☐ Star
- ☐ Three-wheeled board
- ☐ Top hat
- ☐ Turtle
- ☐ Winged board
- ☐ Yo-yo

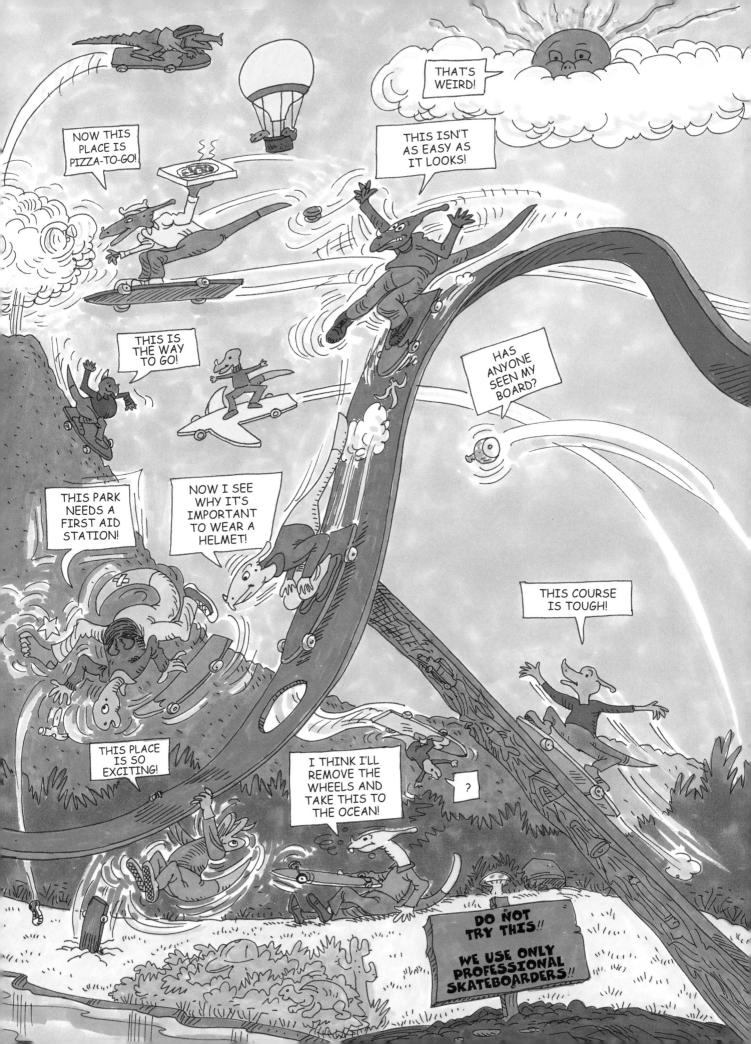

# ROBOTIC -A- SAURS

**FIND THESE ITEMS:**

- ❏ Arrow
- ❏ Balloon
- ❏ Banana peel
- ❏ Bow tie
- ❏ Brush
- ❏ Crystal ball
- ❏ Fire hydrant
- ❏ Hammer
- ❏❏ Hearts
- ❏ Ice cream cone
- ❏ Ice skates
- ❏ Kite
- ❏❏ Light bulbs
- ❏ Loose screw
- ❏ Necktie
- ❏ Oil can
- ❏❏ Pencils
- ❏ Pizza
- ❏ Roller skates
- ❏ Satellite dish
- ❏ Shoulder bag
- ❏ Star
- ❏ Sunglasses
- ❏ Telescope
- ❏ Umbrella
- ❏ Vacuum
- ❏ Yo-yo

# SO YOU WANT TO BE A
## STAR -A- SAURUS

### FIND THESE ITEMS:

- ☐ Beret
- ☐ Bird
- ☐ Bottle
- ☐☐ Bow ties
- ☐ Box
- ☐ Candle
- ☐ Clipboard
- ☐ Crown
- ☐ Dracula-saurus
- ☐ Drum
- ☐ Flower
- ☐ Fork
- ☐ Frying pan
- ☐ Ghost
- ☐ Heart
- ☐ Medal
- ☐☐ Moustaches
- ☐ Pearl necklace
- ☐☐ Pencils
- ☐ Periscope
- ☐☐ Pointy beards
- ☐☐☐ Scarves
- ☐☐ Stars
- ☐☐☐ Sunglasses
- ☐ Sword
- ☐ Ten-gallon hat
- ☐ Tic-tac-toe
- ☐ Ticket
- ☐ Top hat
- ☐ Walking stick

# MARATHON -A- SAURUS

## FIND THESE ITEMS:

- ☐ Automobile
- ☐ Axe
- ☐ Bird
- ☐ Bowling ball
- ☐ Cactus
- ☐ Cell phone
- ☐ Coffee pot
- ☐ Cup
- ☐ Fire hydrant
- ☐ Fish
- ☐ Jack-o-lantern
- ☐ Jester's cap
- ☐ Key
- ☐ Kite
- ☐☐ Lost baseball caps
- ☐ Moustache
- ☐ Pencil
- ☐ Rolling pin
- ☐ Skateboard
- ☐☐ Socks
- ☐ Star
- ☐ Straw
- ☐ Telescope
- ☐ Tent
- ☐ Traffic light
- ☐ Tulip
- ☐ Turtle
- ☐ Volcano

# HARD HAT -A- SAURUS

## FIND THESE ITEMS:

- ▢▢▢▢▢ Arrows
- ▢ Astronaut
- ▢▢▢ Balloons
- ▢ Banana peel
- ▢ Bicycle
- ▢ Book
- ▢ Bowling ball
- ▢ Clothes line
- ▢ Comb
- ▢ Cow
- ▢ Firecracker
- ▢ Fish
- ▢ Fish bowl
- ▢ Football
- ▢▢ Hearts
- ▢ Igloo
- ▢ Lunchbox
- ▢ Moose head
- ▢ Mouse
- ▢ Paint can
- ▢ Sail
- ▢ Saw
- ▢ Scarf
- ▢ Snake
- ▢ Sunglasses
- ▢ Teepee
- ▢ Thermometer
- ▢ Top hat
- ▢ Turtle
- ▢ Used tire
- ▢ Wheel

# THE FAMOUS STORY OF
# FRANKENSAURUS

## FIND THESE ITEMS:

- ☐ Alarm clock
- ☐ Axe
- ☐ Banana peel
- ☐☐ Band-aids
- ☐ Baseball bat
- ☐ Baseball cap
- ☐ Bow and arrow
- ☐ Bowling ball
- ☐ Candle
- ☐ Cupcake
- ☐ Dead flower
- ☐ Drum
- ☐ Eyeglasses
- ☐ Fire hydrant
- ☐ Fish
- ☐ Football
- ☐ Heart
- ☐ Knitting needles
- ☐ Lollipop
- ☐ Oil can
- ☐ Paddle
- ☐ Paper airplane
- ☐☐ Pencils
- ☐ Periscope
- ☐ Pizza
- ☐ Rolling pin
- ☐ Saw
- ☐ Scissors
- ☐ Screwdriver
- ☐ Sunglasses
- ☐ Tape
- ☐ Thermometer
- ☐ Tic-tac-toe
- ☐ Turtle
- ☐ Yo-yo

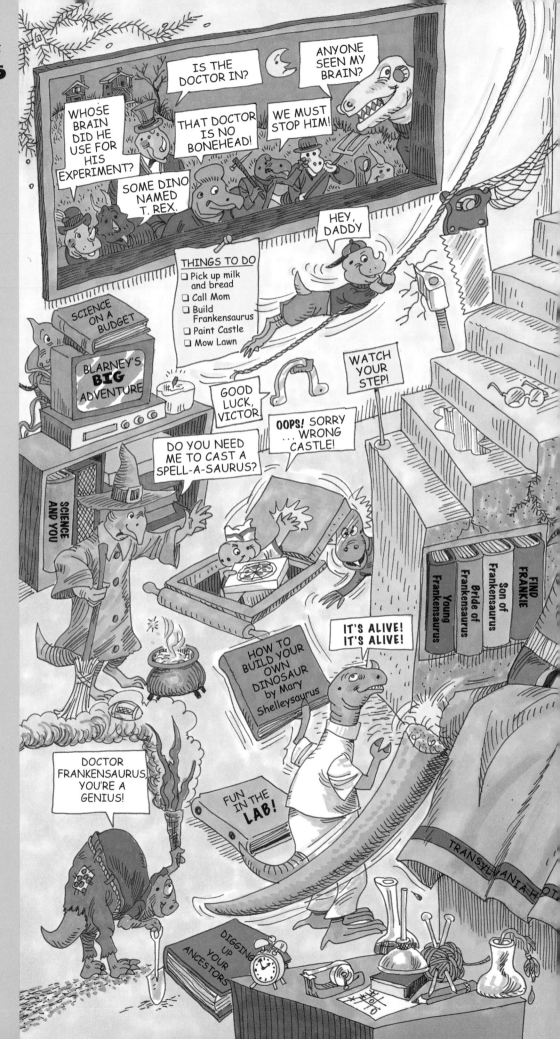

# DINO-WRESTLING
IS REALLY HUGE!

## FIND THESE ITEMS:

- ☐ Band-Aid
- ☐☐☐ Baseball caps
- ☐ Baseball glove
- ☐ Basketball
- ☐ Bow tie
- ☐ Camera
- ☐ Drinking straw
- ☐ Dunce cap
- ☐ Egg
- ☐ Envelope
- ☐ Flowers
- ☐ Harmonica
- ☐☐ Headphones
- ☐ Heart
- ☐ Ice cream cone
- ☐ Kite
- ☐☐ Lost balloons
- ☐ Microphone
- ☐ Necktie
- ☐☐ Pencils
- ☐ Periscope
- ☐ Scarf
- ☐ Slice of pizza
- ☐ Straw hat
- ☐ Sunglasses
- ☐ Telescope
- ☐ Top hat
- ☐ Yo-yo

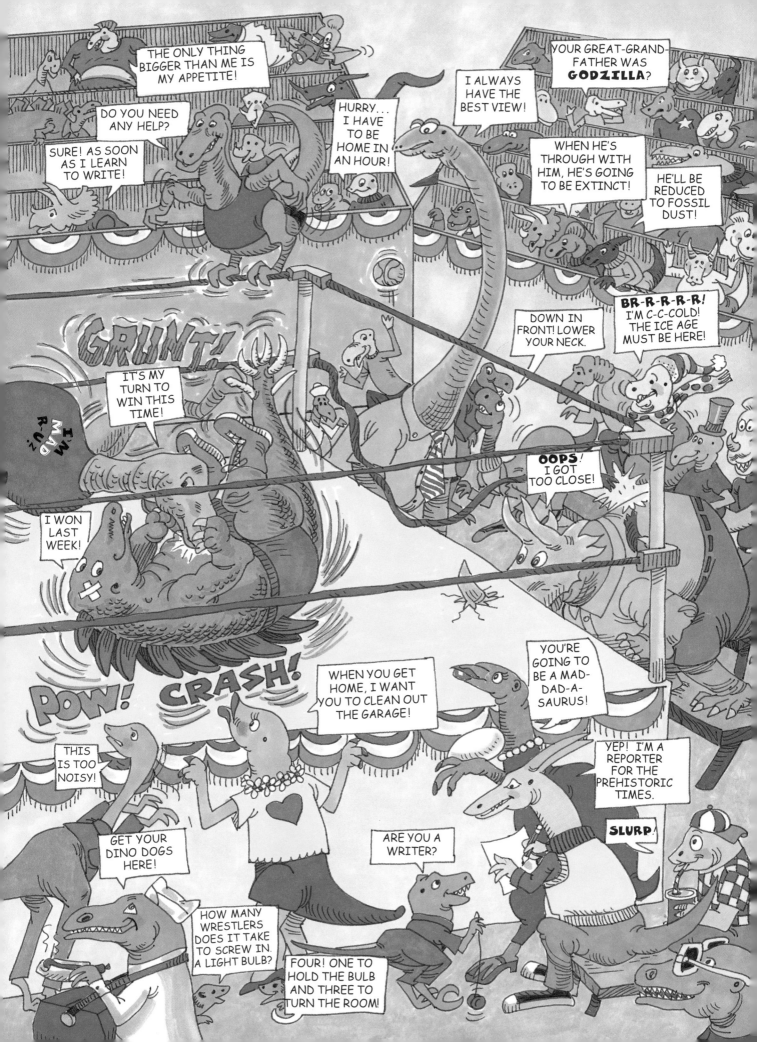

# THE VOYAGE OF CHRISTOPHER COLUMBUSAURUS

**FIND THESE ITEMS:**

- ☐☐☐ Balloons
- ☐ Barber Pole
- ☐☐ Brushes
- ☐ Bullhorn
- ☐ Candle
- ☐ Chef's hat
- ☐ Fire hydrant
- ☐ Fishing rod
- ☐ Fork
- ☐ Heart
- ☐ Horseshoe
- ☐ Hourglass
- ☐ Ice cream cone
- ☐ Key
- ☐ Kite
- ☐ Mermaid
- ☐ Periscope
- ☐ Pie
- ☐ Sock
- ☐ Sunglasses
- ☐ Sailor's cap
- ☐ Telescope
- ☐ Tire
- ☐ Umbrella
- ☐ Yo-yo

# DINOSAURS IN SPACE

## FIND THESE ITEMS:

- ☐ Apple
- ☐ Banana
- ☐ Band-aid
- ☐ Barber pole
- ☐ Baseball
- ☐ Baseball cap
- ☐ Bow tie
- ☐ Cane
- ☐ Carrot
- ☐ Coffee pot
- ☐ Cups
- ☐ Envelopes
- ☐ Flower pot
- ☐ Garden hose
- ☐ Hammer
- ☐ Hitchhiker
- ☐ Ice cream cone
- ☐ Key
- ☐ Kite
- ☐ Lost Shoe
- ☐ Medal
- ☐ Oil can
- ☐ Pencil
- ☐ Saw
- ☐ Screwdriver
- ☐ Shovel
- ☐ Speaker
- ☐ Teepee
- ☐ Telescope
- ☐ Toothbrush
- ☐ Tic-tac-toe

## DINO VACATIONS IN NEW YORK CITY

### FIND THESE ITEMS:

- ☐ Banana
- ☐ Bicycle messenger
- ☐ Bone
- ☐ Paintbrush
- ☐☐☐ Burned-out bulbs
- ☐ Cane
- ☐ Clipboard
- ☐ Clothespin
- ☐ Crayon
- ☐ Envelope
- ☐ Fire hydrants
- ☐ Fork
- ☐ Ghost
- ☐ Hearts
- ☐ Horseshoe
- ☐ Ice cream cone
- ☐ In-line skater
- ☐ Jack-o-lantern
- ☐ Ladder
- ☐ Leaking fire hydrant
- ☐ Lost balloon
- ☐ Mouse
- ☐ Paper airplane
- ☐ Party hat
- ☐ Teepee
- ☐ Worm

# DINOSAURS IN KING ARTHUR'S COURT

## FIND THESE ITEMS:

- ☐ Balloon
- ☐ Banana
- ☐☐ Banana peels
- ☐ Baseball cap
- ☐ Basketball
- ☐ Bell
- ☐ Bird
- ☐ Bone
- ☐ Candle
- ☐ Carrot
- ☐☐☐ Clothespins
- ☐ Earring
- ☐ Feather
- ☐ Heart
- ☐ Ice cream cone
- ☐ Jestersaurus
- ☐ Jugglersaurus
- ☐ Light bulb
- ☐ Lost sword
- ☐ Merlinasaurus
- ☐ Rollerskate
- ☐ Sock
- ☐ Stuck sword
- ☐ Telescope
- ☐ Whale

# DINO SUPERHEROES

**FIND THESE ITEMS:**

- ❏ Arrow
- ❏ Banana peel
- ❏ Bat
- ❏ Bone
- ❏ Cactus
- ❏ Chef's hat
- ❏ Drum
- ❏ Envelope
- ❏ Fish
- ❏ Football
- ❏ Hammer
- ❏ Heart
- ❏ Hot dog
- ❏ Jack-o-lantern
- ❏ Key
- ❏ Kite
- ❏ Owl
- ❏ Paper airplane
- ❏ Pencil
- ❏ Rabbit
- ❏ Screwdriver
- ❏ Seal
- ❏ Straw
- ❏ Television
- ❏ Toothbrush
- ❏ Top hat
- ❏ Umbrella

## WILD WEST TOWN?

**FIND THESE ITEMS:**

- ☐☐ Arrows
- ☐ Axe
- ☐☐ Badges
- ☐ Balloons
- ☐ Banana
- ☐ Barrel
- ☐ Bones
- ☐ Bow Tie
- ☐ Brush
- ☐☐ Cactus
- ☐ Candle
- ☐ Cheese
- ☐☐ Coonskin caps
- ☐ Cup
- ☐☐ Drums
- ☐ Elephant
- ☐ Eyeglasses
- ☐ Fire hydrant
- ☐ Fish
- ☐ Flower
- ☐ Football
- ☐ Heart
- ☐ Horseshoe
- ☐ Pencil
- ☐ Razor
- ☐ Ring
- ☐ Top hat
- ☐ Worm

# PICNIC -A- SAURUS

## FIND THESE ITEMS:

- [ ] Arrow
- [ ] [ ] Baseball caps
- [ ] Bone
- [ ] Cactus
- [ ] Comb
- [ ] Cell phone
- [ ] [ ] Eyeglasses
- [ ] Fish
- [ ] Flower
- [ ] Football
- [ ] [ ] [ ] Forks
- [ ] Four-leaf clover
- [ ] Frog
- [ ] Ghost
- [ ] Hot dog
- [ ] Lamp
- [ ] Lion
- [ ] Lost kite
- [ ] Lost sunglasses
- [ ] Mushroom
- [ ] Pie
- [ ] Pizza delivery dino
- [ ] Propeller
- [ ] Ring
- [ ] Salt shaker
- [ ] Star
- [ ] Yo-yo

# A DAY AT
# DINO-LAND

## FIND THESE ITEMS:

- ☐ Bone
- ☐ Bow tie
- ☐ Fire hydrant
- ☐ Fish
- ☐ Flower
- ☐ Flowerpot
- ☐ Football
- ☐ Heart
- ☐ Hot-air balloon
- ☐ Necktie
- ☐ Net
- ☐ Pencil
- ☐ Periscope
- ☐ Pick
- ☐ Pizza delivery dino
- ☐ Plunger
- ☐ Screwdriver
- ☐ Shark fin
- ☐ Shovel
- ☐ Skier
- ☐ Sled
- ☐ Sunglasses
- ☐ Suspenders
- ☐ Tire
- ☐ Turtle

## DINO-5... IN CONCERT

### FIND THESE ITEMS:

- ☐ Accordion
- ☐ Apple
- ☐ Arrow
- ☐ Astronaut
- ☐ Bandana
- ☐ Basketball
- ☐ Bell
- ☐ Beret
- ☐ Cane
- ☐ Carrot
- ☐ Crayon
- ☐ Empty bird cage
- ☐ Fish
- ☐☐☐ Hearts
- ☐ Key
- ☐ Light bulb
- ☐ Lost balloon
- ☐ Moon face
- ☐ Monocle
- ☐ Moustache
- ☐ Paintbrush
- ☐ Pear
- ☐ Pencil
- ☐ Pizza delivery dino
- ☐ Sailor cap
- ☐ Seal
- ☐ Straw
- ☐ Sunglasses
- ☐ Teapot
- ☐ Thermometer
- ☐ Top hat
- ☐ Whistler

LAST ONE IN IS A
# ROTTENSAURUS EGG

### FIND THESE ITEMS:

- ☐☐ Balloons
- ☐☐☐ Baseball caps
- ☐ Bird
- ☐ Book
- ☐ Boombox
- ☐ Bone
- ☐ Bowling ball
- ☐ Fire hydrant
- ☐ Flashlight
- ☐ Football
- ☐ Golf club
- ☐ Hammer
- ☐ Horseshoe
- ☐ Ice cream cone
- ☐ Lamp
- ☐ Mushroom
- ☐ Paper airplane
- ☐☐ Periscopes
- ☐ Pizza delivery dino
- ☐ Ring
- ☐ Sailor cap
- ☐☐ Shark fins
- ☐ Starfish
- ☐☐ Sunglasses
- ☐ Telescope
- ☐ Top hat
- ☐ TV set

# SCHOOL-YARDASAURUS

**FIND THESE ITEMS:**

- ☐ Balloon
- ☐ Banana peel
- ☐ Beret
- ☐☐ Bones
- ☐ Bow tie
- ☐ Broom
- ☐ Butterfly
- ☐ Camera
- ☐ Coon-skin cap
- ☐ Drum
- ☐ Drum major
- ☐☐ Eyeglasses
- ☐ Fish
- ☐ Heart
- ☐ Hot dog
- ☐ Juggler
- ☐ Kite
- ☐ Lit candle
- ☐ Lollipop
- ☐ Lost cookie
- ☐ Lost sneakers
- ☐ Mailbox
- ☐ Paper airplane
- ☐ Pizza delivery dino
- ☐ Sailor cap
- ☐ Skate
- ☐ Star
- ☐ Sunglasses
- ☐ Tennis racket
- ☐ Tuba
- ☐ Yo-yo

# STAND-UP DINO

**FIND THESE ITEMS:**

- ❏ Airplane
- ❏ Anchor
- ❏ Apple
- ❏ Barrel
- ❏ Baseball bat
- ❏ Binoculars
- ❏ Bone
- ❏ Burned-out bulb
- ❏ Candle
- ❏ Chicken
- ❏ Clothespin
- ❏❏❏❏❏ Cups
- ❏ Earring
- ❏❏ Fish
- ❏ Football
- ❏ Heart
- ❏ Hot dog
- ❏ Kite
- ❏ Mailbox
- ❏ Monocle
- ❏ Moustache
- ❏❏ Pencils
- ❏ Pizza delivery dino
- ❏ Sailboat
- ❏ Sled
- ❏ Sunglasses

# MUSEUM-SAURUS

## FIND THESE ITEMS:

- ❏ Arrow
- ❏ Astronaut
- ❏ Bib
- ❏ Broom
- ❏ Camera
- ❏ Cane
- ❏ Crack
- ❏ Crown
- ❏ Dart
- ❏ Eyeglasses
- ❏ Fish
- ❏ Flower
- ❏ Golf clubs
- ❏ Heart
- ❏ Hourglass
- ❏ Menu
- ❏ Moustache
- ❏ Nail
- ❏❏❏ Pencils
- ❏ Pizza delivery dino
- ❏ Rock
- ❏ Roll
- ❏ Telescope
- ❏ Toothbrush
- ❏ Top hat
- ❏ Umbrella
- ❏ Volcano
- ❏ Yo-yo

## ZOOASAURUS

**FIND THESE ITEMS:**

- ☐ Anchor tattoo
- ☐ Banana peel
- ☐ Baseball cap
- ☐ Beret
- ☐ Bird
- ☐ Birdhouse
- ☐ Bow tie
- ☐ Camera
- ☐ Cell phone
- ☐ Cupcake
- ☐ Eyeglasses
- ☐ Fallen ice cream cone
- ☐ Flower
- ☐ Heart
- ☐ Ice cream pop
- ☐ Lost sock
- ☐ Star
- ☐ ☐ Sunglasses

# DINOSAURS
## LOST IN TIME

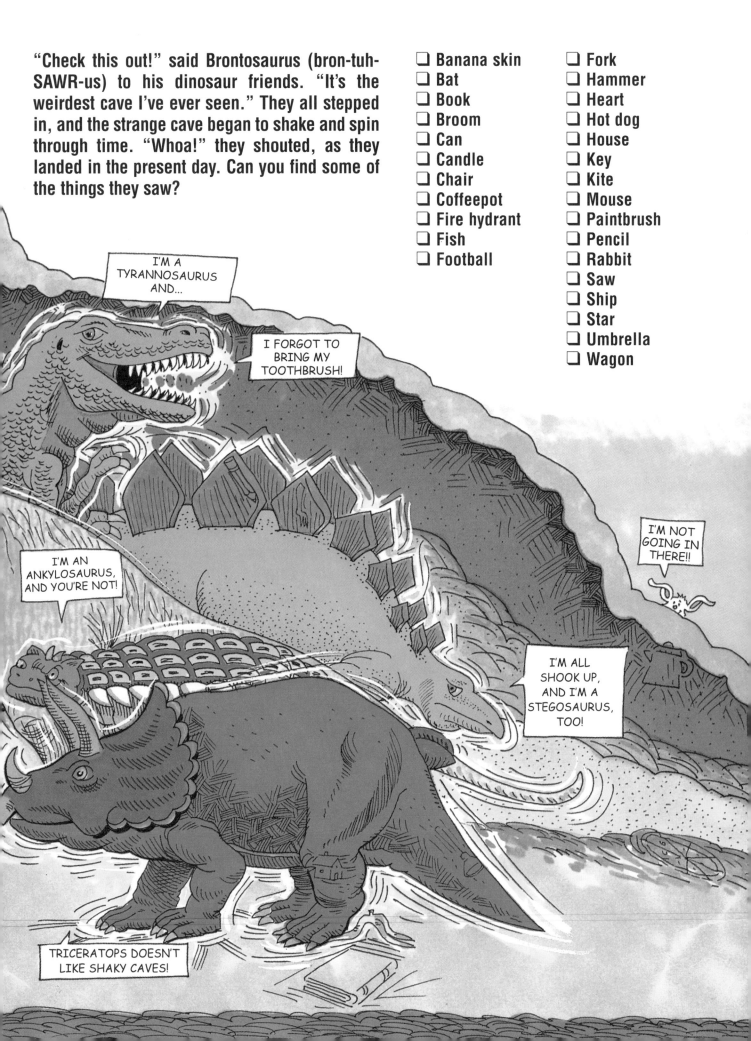

"Check this out!" said Brontosaurus (bron-tuh-SAWR-us) to his dinosaur friends. "It's the weirdest cave I've ever seen." They all stepped in, and the strange cave began to shake and spin through time. "Whoa!" they shouted, as they landed in the present day. Can you find some of the things they saw?

❑ Banana skin
❑ Bat
❑ Book
❑ Broom
❑ Can
❑ Candle
❑ Chair
❑ Coffeepot
❑ Fire hydrant
❑ Fish
❑ Football

❑ Fork
❑ Hammer
❑ Heart
❑ Hot dog
❑ House
❑ Key
❑ Kite
❑ Mouse
❑ Paintbrush
❑ Pencil
❑ Rabbit
❑ Saw
❑ Ship
❑ Star
❑ Umbrella
❑ Wagon

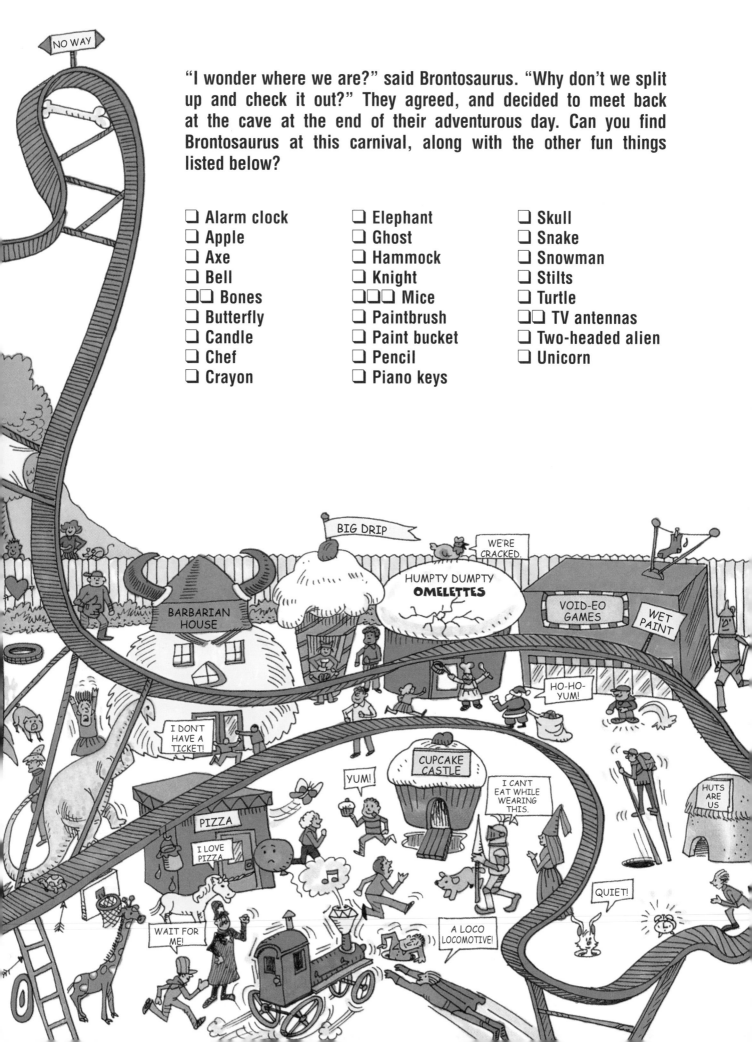

"I wonder where we are?" said Brontosaurus. "Why don't we split up and check it out?" They agreed, and decided to meet back at the cave at the end of their adventurous day. Can you find Brontosaurus at this carnival, along with the other fun things listed below?

- ❑ Alarm clock
- ❑ Apple
- ❑ Axe
- ❑ Bell
- ❑❑ Bones
- ❑ Butterfly
- ❑ Candle
- ❑ Chef
- ❑ Crayon

- ❑ Elephant
- ❑ Ghost
- ❑ Hammock
- ❑ Knight
- ❑❑❑ Mice
- ❑ Paintbrush
- ❑ Paint bucket
- ❑ Pencil
- ❑ Piano keys

- ❑ Skull
- ❑ Snake
- ❑ Snowman
- ❑ Stilts
- ❑ Turtle
- ❑❑ TV antennas
- ❑ Two-headed alien
- ❑ Unicorn

"This place sounds really crazy," said Compsognathus (komp-so-NAY-thus). "I wonder what's going on?" Can you find Brontosaurus and Compsognathus at this rock concert? Don't forget to look for the following fun things, too.

- ❑ Bell
- ❑ Bird cage
- ❑ Candle
- ❑ Chef's hat
- ❑ Chicken drumstick
- ❑ Crown
- ❑ Elephant
- ❑ Fish
- ❑ Hammer
- ❑ Heart
- ❑ Horseshoe
- ❑ Ice cream cone
- ❑ Mermaid
- ❑ Mouse
- ❑ Octopus
- ❑ Owl
- ❑ Paper airplane
- ❑ Pencil
- ❑ Pie
- ❑ Rabbit
- ❑ Saw
- ❑ Skate
- ❑ Snail
- ❑ Sock
- ❑ Star
- ❑ Turtle
- ❑ Worm

"Oh, cool! But where am I?" said Triceratops (try-SAIR-uh-tops). "Hey! I see some of my friends." Can you find Brontosaurus, Triceratops, and Compsognathus (komp-so-NAY-thus) at this skating rink? Don't forget to look for the following fun things, too!

- ❏ Alligator
- ❏ Bone
- ❏ Bowling ball
- ❏ Broom
- ❏❏ Cactuses
- ❏❏ Cameras
- ❏ Crutch
- ❏ Elf
- ❏ Football player
- ❏ Humpty Dumpty
- ❏ Hungry monster
- ❏ Ice skateboard
- ❏ Igloo
- ❏ Kangaroo
- ❏ Lost mitten
- ❏ Mouse
- ❏ Necklace
- ❏ Panda
- ❏❏ Penguins
- ❏ Pillow
- ❏ Roller skates
- ❏ Santa Claus
- ❏ Shark fin
- ❏ Skier
- ❏ Straw basket
- ❏ Top hat
- ❏ TV set

"Yum! Something smells good," said Iguanodon (ig-WAN-oh-don). "Maybe I'll give up eating plants." Can you find Brontosaurus, Triceratops, Compsognathus, and Iguanodon at this fast-food stand? Don't forget to look for the following fun things, too!

- ❏ Apple
- ❏ Astronaut
- ❏ Candy cane
- ❏ Chicken
- ❏ Clown
- ❏ Count Dracula
- ❏ Diver
- ❏ Doctor
- ❏ Dog
- ❏ Doughnut
- ❏ Duck
- ❏ Fish
- ❏ Monster
- ❏ Moose head
- ❏ Mouse
- ❏ Mustache
- ❏ Penguin
- ❏ Pinocchio
- ❏ Propeller
- ❏ Seal
- ❏ Star
- ❏❏ Straws
- ❏ Surfer
- ❏ Torn bag
- ❏ Turtle
- ❏ Unicycle
- ❏ Viking

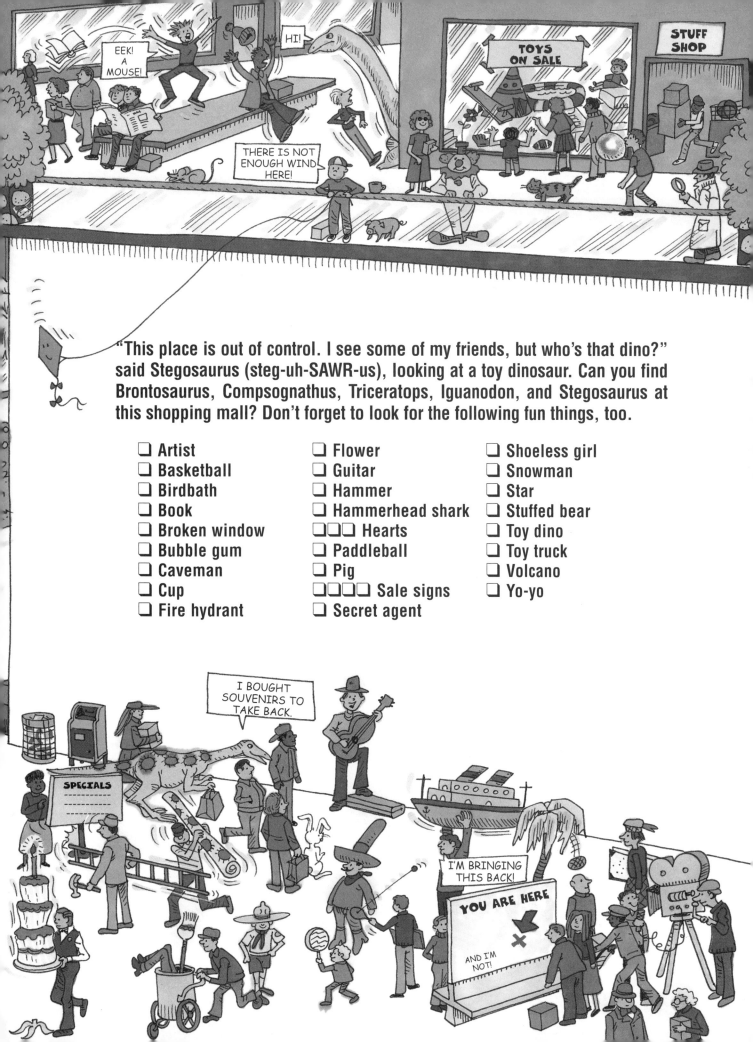

"This place is out of control. I see some of my friends, but who's that dino?" said Stegosaurus (steg-uh-SAWR-us), looking at a toy dinosaur. Can you find Brontosaurus, Compsognathus, Triceratops, Iguanodon, and Stegosaurus at this shopping mall? Don't forget to look for the following fun things, too.

- ❏ Artist
- ❏ Basketball
- ❏ Birdbath
- ❏ Book
- ❏ Broken window
- ❏ Bubble gum
- ❏ Caveman
- ❏ Cup
- ❏ Fire hydrant
- ❏ Flower
- ❏ Guitar
- ❏ Hammer
- ❏ Hammerhead shark
- ❏❏❏ Hearts
- ❏ Paddleball
- ❏ Pig
- ❏❏❏❏ Sale signs
- ❏ Secret agent
- ❏ Shoeless girl
- ❏ Snowman
- ❏ Star
- ❏ Stuffed bear
- ❏ Toy dino
- ❏ Toy truck
- ❏ Volcano
- ❏ Yo-yo

"Look at all those little creatures! They seem to know where they're going," said Diplodocus (dih-PLOD-uh-kus). "Maybe they can tell me where I am." Can you find Brontosaurus, Compsognathus, Triceratops, Iguanodon, Stegosaurus, and Diplodocus? Don't forget to look for the following fun things, too.

- ❑ Airplane
- ❑ Apple
- ❑ Arrow
- ❑❑❑ Balloons
- ❑ Baseball
- ❑ Calendar
- ❑ Carrot
- ❑ Cat
- ❑ Coonskin cap

- ❑ Crown
- ❑ Elephant
- ❑ Football helmet
- ❑ Golf club
- ❑ Hockey stick
- ❑❑ Kites
- ❑ Lunch box
- ❑ Oil can
- ❑ Pyramid

- ❑ Rocket ship
- ❑ Roller skate
- ❑ Sailor cap
- ❑ Scissors
- ❑ Straw
- ❑ Unicorn
- ❑ Van
- ❑ Watering can

"I don't like this place at all," said Deinonychus (dyne-ON-ik-us). "There are too many strange creatures. I'm getting out of here quick." Can you find Brontosaurus, Triceratops, Compsognathus, Iguanodon, Stegosaurus, Diplodocus, Coelophysis, and Deinonychus at this zoo? Don't forget to look for the following fun things, too!

- ❑ Aardvark
- ❑ Alien
- ❑ Anteater
- ❑ Arrow
- ❑ Baseball glove
- ❑ Bat
- ❑ Beaver
- ❑ Bighorn
- ❑ Bottle
- ❑ Butterfly
- ❑ Candle
- ❑ Clown
- ❑ Dog
- ❑ Duck
- ❑ Kangaroo
- ❑ Lost balloon
- ❑ Moose
- ❑ Net
- ❑❑ Owls
- ❑ Panda
- ❑ Polar Bear
- ❑ Raccoon
- ❑ Rhinoceros
- ❑ Sick animal
- ❑ Singing cactus
- ❑❑ Snakes
- ❑ Toucan
- ❑❑❑ Umbrellas
- ❑ Wolf
- ❑ Yak

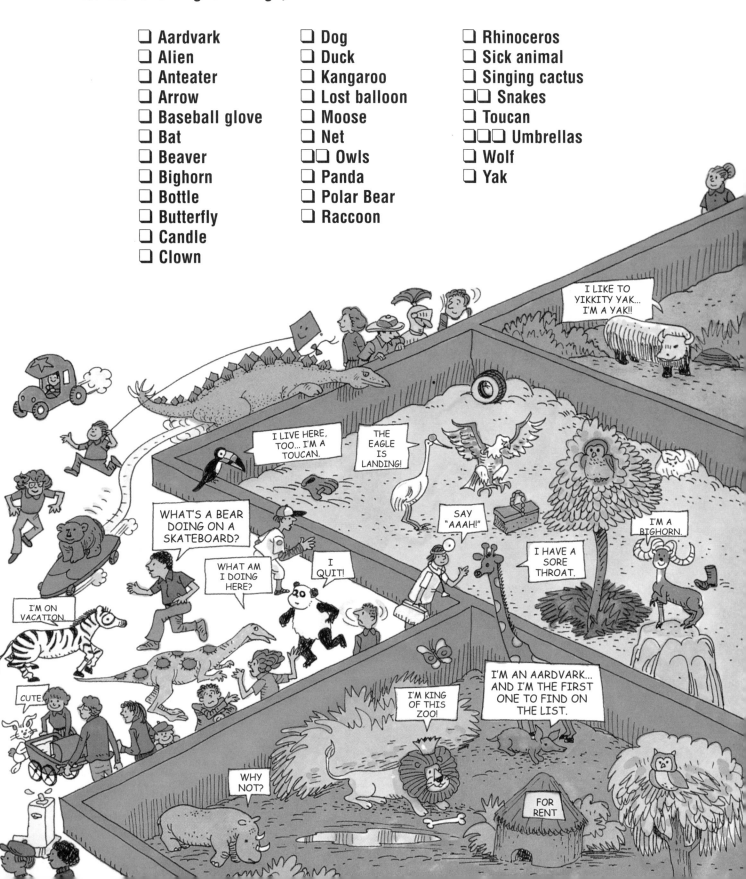

"Hey, this place is wild!" said Tyrannosaurus (tye-RAN-uh-sawr-us). "This guy looks just like me, but why is he so small?" Can you find Brontosaurus, Triceratops, Compsognathus, Iguanodon, Stegosaurus, Diplodocus, Coelophysis, Deinonychus, and Tyrannosaurus at this toy store? Don't forget to look for the following fun things, too!

❑ Anchor
❑ Arrow
❑ Basketball
❑ Blimp
❑ Block
❑❑❑ Bow ties
❑ Camel
❑ Carrot
❑❑❑❑ Cars
❑ Crown
❑ Dart

❑ Duck cap
❑ Fishing pole
❑ Ghost
❑ Golf club
❑ Jack-in-the-box
❑ Mask
❑ Mouse
❑ Mushroom
❑ Palm tree
❑ Pencil
❑ Piggy bank

❑ Robot waiter
❑ Rocking chair
❑ Skate
❑ Skeleton
❑ Tepee
❑ Unicorn
❑ Whistle
❑ Wind-up volcano
❑ Yo-yo
❑ Zebra

"Oh, wow! What are those things flying in the air?" wondered Ankylosaurus (an-kil-uh-SAWR-us). Can you find Brontosaurus, Compsognathus, Triceratops, Iguanodon, Stegosaurus, Diplodocus, Coelophysis, Deinonychus, Tyrannosaurus, and Ankylosaurus at this big-balloon parade? Don't forget to look for the following fun things, too.

- ❑❑ Birds
- ❑ Broom
- ❑ Candy cane
- ❑ Clown
- ❑ Coffeepot
- ❑ Cooking pot
- ❑ Cow
- ❑ Deflated balloon
- ❑ Dummy mummy
- ❑ Fire hydrant
- ❑ Fish
- ❑ Giant
- ❑ Hammer
- ❑❑❑❑ Happy stars
- ❑ Humpty Dumpty
- ❑❑ Ice skates (2 pairs)
- ❑ King Kong
- ❑ Kite
- ❑ Knight
- ❑ Lion
- ❑ Mouse
- ❑ Paintbrush
- ❑ Penguin
- ❑ Pirate
- ❑❑ Rabbits
- ❑ Scarecrow
- ❑ Ship
- ❑ Skier
- ❑ Sore feet
- ❑ Three little pigs
- ❑❑ Turtles
- ❑ Unicyclist

"Here we are, back in this weird cave," said Brontosaurus. "It's really wacky around here. I'm ready to go home, back to prehistoric times." The dinosaurs looked at one another. "But how?" they asked. Before Brontosaurus could answer, the cave shook. Once again the dino friends were traveling through time. But did they make it home? Or did they land in another time and place?